THE CROWN

Alexis, son of Leon, knows it is a wonderful time to be an Athenian. It is the fifth century BC, and Athens is the finest city-state in Greece, famous for its democracy, its Theatre Festival, and its beautiful Acropolis hill – the city's crown of violet.

It's a wonderful time for a boy, of course, but not so much fun for a girl. Athenian women must stay at home, must not talk to men, must not have intelligent conversations about politics or plays. So when Alexis makes friends with Corinna, a girl *and* a foreigner, they have to meet in a secret cave in the hills. There, Alexis writes a play, a comedy called *The Gadfly*, and he and Corinna plan how to enter it for the next year's Theatre Festival.

Then they learn that Athens is in danger, from men both inside and outside the city, who are planning a revolution to bring the famous Athenian democracy to an end . . .

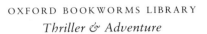

OXFORD BOOKWORMS LIBRARY
Thriller & Adventure

The Crown of Violet

Stage 3 (1000 headwords)

Series Editor: Jennifer Bassett
Founder Editor: Tricia Hedge
Activities Editors: Jennifer Bassett and Alison Baxter

Great Athens, shining town
Of song, with violet crown . . .

PINDAR

GEOFFREY TREASE

The Crown of Violet

Retold by
John Escott

Illustrated by
Cory

OXFORD UNIVERSITY PRESS

OXFORD

UNIVERSITY PRESS

Great Clarendon Street, Oxford OX2 6DP

Oxford University Press is a department of the University of Oxford.
It furthers the University's objective of excellence in research, scholarship,
and education by publishing worldwide in

Oxford New York

Auckland Cape Town Dar es Salaam Hong Kong Karachi
Kuala Lumpur Madrid Melbourne Mexico City Nairobi
New Delhi Shanghai Taipei Toronto

With offices in

Argentina Austria Brazil Chile Czech Republic France Greece
Guatemala Hungary Italy Japan Poland Portugal Singapore
South Korea Switzerland Thailand Turkey Ukraine Vietnam

OXFORD and OXFORD ENGLISH are registered trade marks of
Oxford University Press in the UK and in certain other countries

Text © Geoffrey Trease 1952
Original edition published by Macmillan Publishers Ltd
This simplified edition © Oxford University Press 2008

Database right Oxford University Press (maker)

First published in Oxford Bookworms 1997

2 4 6 8 10 9 7 5 3 1

ISBN 978 0 19 479114 4

Printed in Hong Kong

Illustrated by: Cory/Portland Studios, Greenville, USA

Word count (main text): 10,800 words

For more information on the Oxford Bookworms Library,
visit www.oup.com/elt/bookworms

CONTENTS

A VISIT TO THE THEATRE

'No school today! Wonderful! Wonderful!'

Alexis woke up suddenly, to find his noisy young brother shouting in his ear.

'Do you realize what day it is?' asked Theo.

Alexis sat up quickly. 'Oh! The Theatre Festival!'

He jumped up and looked out of the window. The sky over Athens had turned from dark blue to grey, and people all over the city were waking up.

Soon all the family were dressed in their best clothes

Alexis looked out of the window.

1

and ready to leave. Alexis, in a new white tunic, went in front with his father, Leon, and his brother. Behind them came his mother and Nico, his older sister. Both wore veils over their faces – on Father's orders. He thought that a woman's place was in the home and did not really like them going out into the city.

As they walked through the narrow streets of the city in the early golden sunlight, Alexis thought how lovely Athens looked. Hundreds of people were already going into the theatre – Athenians, foreigners from the western islands, Cretans, Egyptians . . . People from every country came to Athens for the Theatre Festival. 'And why not?' Alexis thought. 'Athens is the finest city-state in Greece.'

Inside the theatre Alexis' family joined the crowd climbing up the terraces to find seats.

'These will be fine,' said Father. They sat down and were getting comfortable when a tall young man came up to them. He had long hair and wore a bright red cloak, high boots, and gold rings.

'This is *my* seat,' he said. 'You'll have to move.'

Father looked at him coldly. 'I suppose from the way you speak that you are from Athens, although your hair is as long as a Spartan's. But if you are an Athenian, you should know that these seats are for anyone to sit in.'

'I was here first! I only went to speak to someone for a moment. Are you going to move or not?'

'I am not.' Father looked round. 'There is a place for you a little way behind us.'

The young man's face became very red, but he moved angrily to the empty seat behind.

'Who was he?' Nico asked Father.

'His name is Hippias,' said Father. 'I know his kind. Too much money and nothing to do!'

'This is my seat,' the young man said. 'You'll have to move.'

For the rest of the morning, the high narrow stage became Alexis' world – the music, the dancing, and the wonderful words of the actors. Alexis liked to write plays himself, but he did it secretly.

The tragedies – the sad plays – went on until the middle of the day, and after lunch came the comedies.

'Now it's time for the funny plays,' said Theo. 'Don't you wish you could stay, Nico?'

Nico looked cross, and Mother said quickly, 'Comedies are not for ladies. Many of the jokes are not – not polite.'

'And the plays are about politics,' said Father, 'which is boring for ladies.'

'Are you bored by politics?' Theo asked Nico.

'How do I know?' said Nico, with an angry look. 'I never see the plays, do I?'

Alexis watched his mother and Nico leave. To him, it didn't seem right that women had to miss the comedies.

Ω Ω Ω

The first comedy did not amuse people, and the audience threw things and shouted at the actors to tell them this.

'How awful for them,' said Alexis, '*and* for the writer. I wonder how he's feeling?'

The second comedy was much better. Alexis loved all the jokes about famous people, and his eyes were full of excitement when it finished.

'I think I'll write a comedy,' he told Theo. 'Listen to this.' And, speaking in a high, unnatural voice, he said: '*Do you not know who I am? I'm Hippias!*' Then, changing his voice, he answered himself: '*With your long hair, I thought you were a girl.*'

Theo, who was easily amused, laughed loudly, and Alexis continued with some more lines. Suddenly, and too late, he saw the angry face of Hippias watching them. And he knew in that moment he had made an enemy.

═ 2 ═

CORINNA

Life was quiet after the Festival. Theo returned to school, but Alexis had finished school lessons and was now studying public speaking with a teacher called Milon.

'But I don't *want* to make public speeches,' Alexis had told his father.

'You don't know that yet,' Leon had replied. 'You're clever with words, and if you go into politics, you'll find your public speaking lessons very useful.'

On the day after the Festival Alexis went to Milon's house, but Milon had a headache and was not seeing students that day. Alexis was not sorry. The lessons were hard work and he was very happy to have some free time.

He went to find his friend, Lucian. Half an hour later the two boys were walking out of the city.

'Let's go to the river and swim,' said Lucian.

The water was cold, but they swam for a while and then dressed and went on up the valley into the hills.

5

'Did I hear a flute?' Lucian said, stopping suddenly.

'I can't hear one,' said Alexis. 'Perhaps it was a bird.'

They were on a high rock when Lucian stopped again. 'Listen!' he said. And then Alexis heard the flute in the valley below. He ran down to the trees at the water's edge – and saw a girl holding a flute on the other side of the river. For a moment she looked frightened, then smiled. Lucian came down and joined Alexis.

'Are there any more of you?' the girl asked.

'Just us,' said Alexis. 'You needn't be afraid.'

'I'm not afraid,' she said. She wore a short green dress, and her hair was dark and wet from swimming.

'We ought to go back,' said Lucian. 'I'm hungry—'

'Hungry? Poor boy!' the girl laughed. 'Have a fig – here, catch!' But the fig fell into the river. 'Come over, if you want to. I've got plenty more. There's an easy way, across those rocks up there.'

Soon they were sitting beside her, happily eating figs. Her name was Corinna, and she had just come to live in Athens. Before that she had lived in Syracuse in Sicily.

'But Mum always wanted to come back,' she said.

'Back?' said Alexis. 'Are you Athenians?'

'Oh, no. I don't know what we are! I was born in Athens, but we moved away when I was a baby.'

'They're foreigners,' Lucian said. He looked down his nose at her. 'Not Athenians.'

'But you must be pleased to be in Athens,' Alexis said quickly. He knew Lucian did not like foreigners very much.

'Have a fig – here, catch!'

'Not really,' Corinna said. 'In fact, I hate the place.'

Both boys stared at her. How could anyone hate Athens?

'Girls have an awful time here,' she went on. 'They can't *do* anything. In other Greek cities they can go out, play sports, talk to men – even write plays if they want to.'

'But what does your father say when you run around the hills like this?' asked Alexis.

'I don't have a father,' said Corinna. 'I think he died when I was a baby. Mum has an inn. She's a wonderful cook. It's on the corner of the market-place, where the road turns up to the Acropolis.'

7

'Oh, I know,' said Alexis. 'I live near there.'

He was silent for a moment. It was already clear that Corinna was not an Athenian young lady. But to live in an *inn*, to have a mother who was a cook . . . Lucian looked down his nose again. Inns were usually dirty, noisy places, and well-born Athenian families never went into them.

'I don't like the inn much,' said Corinna. 'That's why I come up to the hills when I can. I've got a secret cave. Do you want to see it? You must promise not to tell anyone.'

She took them to a place where the rock was the colour

The secret cave was hidden by a tall tree.

8

of a violet – the colour of the Acropolis hill, which is why people called Athens 'the city of the violet crown'. Then, suddenly, Corinna disappeared. A few seconds later the boys heard the flute, and saw her high up on a flat rock.

'Use that tree to climb up!' she called to them.

The secret cave was hidden by a tall tree. 'The cave goes a long way back. Can we go and see?' said Lucian.

'It's not safe,' Corinna said. 'There are rock falls.'

'I'm more than happy to stay here in your entrance-hall, and to look out at the sea,' said Alexis.

She laughed. 'You do talk strangely.'

'I'll teach *you* to talk strangely, if you like,' he said seriously. 'And I mean good Athenian Greek.'

'Perhaps I don't want to speak Athenian,' she said. 'But I'd like to read and write better. Will you teach me that?'

'All right,' he said. 'And you can teach me to play the flute. I've always wanted to learn.'

'We ought to go,' Lucian said suddenly. 'It's getting late.'

So the boys said goodbye, climbed down, and began to walk home down the river valley.

'We can go back to the cave when she isn't there,' said Lucian. 'You can't want to see *her* again. A girl like that, a foreigner, living at an inn! I thought she was *terrible*!'

Alexis hit him across the face. A moment later the two friends were fighting on the ground.

'Say you're sorry!' said Lucian, sitting on Alexis.

'I'm – sorry – sorry that you're sitting on my – stomach!' said Alexis, half-laughing.

'And sorry that you hit my face? Yes or no? Or I'll pretend that this is the torch race!' They were both going to be in a boys' horse race soon. Lucian jumped up and down on Alexis' stomach, pretending to be a rider.

'Y–y–yes!' Alexis said at last. 'But only because you're bigger than me!'

Ω Ω Ω

There were ten teams of riders in the boys' torch race. It was a relay race at night – where the burning torch was passed from one rider to the next in each team, and the first team to finish was the winner. Lucian and Alexis practised riding and passing the torch for several days. Then Alexis wanted to stop practising, because he wanted some free time for other things. But when he said this, Lucian looked angry.

'What things?' he said. 'Don't tell me. You want to see that girl again!'

Alexis stared. It was true that he liked Corinna and had found her amusing, but he had not seen her again since the day at the cave. He wanted some time to start writing a play – a tragedy about a famous Greek called Achilles.

Now he became angry too. 'I don't have to explain what I do to you!'

So the two friends did not practise again, and were still cool with each other when the night came for the race.

Both boys were riding for the Leontis team. Alexis, who was number five in the relay, had to ride along the road under the city walls, where most of the crowds were. As he waited with his horse at the change-over place, he saw Hippias in the crowd near him, talking with another man. The stranger wore a large working-man's hat, low over his face. Alexis heard a few words of their conversation.

'. . . very dangerous!' Hippias was saying.

'It was worth the danger,' said the other man. He had a gentleman's voice. 'And it's not so dangerous in the dark.'

So, it was safer in the dark, was it? Alexis listened hard, but could hear no more. What were they planning? And what kind of gentleman wore a working-man's hat?

Suddenly he saw the light of torches against the dark sky, getting bigger and brighter as they came nearer.

'Here they come!' someone shouted, and Alexis moved his horse forward a little.

A boy from the Acamantis team arrived first, and he quickly passed his torch to the next rider in his team.

And in that second or two of light, Alexis saw the face of the stranger with Hippias – an unforgettable face, with deep eyes and a long nose.

But now the next two riders were coming. The first, from the Pandionis team, quickly passed his torch. Then a torch was pushed into Alexis' hand, and he rode away fast.

It was not an easy ride, galloping as fast as possible through the dark, on a rough stony road, with a burning torch in one hand. Alexis started a metre behind the Pandionis rider but slowly got closer and closer. Now he was beside him, now a little in front. Trees flew by, faces appeared and disappeared, voices shouted . . . Suddenly

Alexis saw the face of the stranger . . .

Alexis realized that they were at the change-over place already. He called out the name of his team. 'Leontis!'

'Leontis here!' screamed Lucian.

By now Alexis was a metre in front, but he almost

dropped the torch when passing it to Lucian, and Lucian started a metre behind the new Pandionis rider.

'It was my mistake!' cried Alexis.

The Pandionis team won, with Leontis second. After the race Alexis looked for Lucian but could not find him.

'I think Lucian went home the other way,' a boy told him. He did not look at Alexis.

'Thanks. I understand,' said Alexis sadly.

=== 3 ===

SOCRATES THE GADFLY

The next morning Alexis went to find Lucian and to say sorry. They met in the street, but a few seconds later they were arguing again. Lucian said that he was not interested in Alexis' secrets. He preferred to take sport seriously, he said, and Alexis, clearly, preferred talking to girls in inns.

This made Alexis very angry, and he decided that he *would* go and see Corinna. He also decided not to go to his lesson with Milon. He didn't want to practise public speaking; he just wanted a friend to talk to.

The inn on the corner of the market-place looked bright and clean. Alexis knocked on the door and a very large, red-faced woman opened it.

'I'm – I'm looking for Corinna,' said Alexis.

'She's gone to see Cephalus,' the woman said.

'The sculptor?'

'That's him.' She went back into the kitchen and returned with a small cake. 'Here, have one of these.'

'Thank you,' said Alexis. It was still warm, and very good to eat. 'Are you Corinna's mother?' he asked.

'That's right. Gorgo's my name. How did you guess?' She laughed. 'Do we look alike?'

'Oh, no,' said Alexis. 'I mean – it was the cake. Corinna said what a wonderful cook you are.'

Gorgo looked pleased. 'Best cook in Syracuse, they used to say. Have another cake.'

'No, thank you very much. I have to go now.'

Ω Ω Ω

Alexis looked round the door of the sculptor's workroom. It was an untidy place, with bits of stone all over the floor, and statues all round the walls, some finished, some half-finished. Cephalus was a little man with a beard, and his fingers worked quickly and cleverly on the statue in front of him. Every few seconds, with his eyes half-closed and his head on one side, he stopped to look at the girl standing a few metres away. Corinna was standing very still, holding a bow and pretending to run.

She jumped when she saw Alexis, and Cephalus turned to look. Alexis explained that he was only looking for Corinna. Cephalus turned back to Corinna. 'All right, my dear. That's enough for today. You're tired, and I must go to the market-place now.' He saw Alexis looking at a statue of a man by the wall, and smiled. 'Yes, my boy, that's one of my best statues. I did it years ago, and it was supposed to stand in the middle of the city.'

'Who is it, sir?' asked Alexis, staring at the statue's face.

'Magnes, the man who planned a revolution here in Athens, with the Spartans' help. The City Council will put him to death if he shows his face in Athens again, so his statue isn't wanted.'

'Why do you keep it here?' asked Corinna.

'Magnes has rich friends,' Cephalus said. 'In politics anything can happen. We may live to see him back in Athens, giving orders to us all. And if that ever happens,

'Yes, my boy, that's one of my best statues.'

what will he say if he finds that I've put his statue out with the rubbish?'

Alexis was silent as he and Corinna walked out into the street. He was thinking hard. He had seen that face very recently – those deep eyes, that long nose – under a working-man's hat, in the light of a burning torch.

'I thought,' said Corinna, smiling, 'that you wanted to talk to me. But you haven't said a word.'

'Sorry,' said Alexis. 'I've just had a surprise. That man Magnes – I saw him last night, at the torch race, talking to a man called Hippias, a rich Athenian.'

'Oh!' said Corinna. 'What's he doing in Athens?'

'That's what *I'd* like to know. What shall I do?'

'Tell your father,' she said.

'Yes, but I'm supposed to be at Milon's lesson. And how can I explain why I was at Cephalus' workroom?'

'Looking for me, you mean? A most unsuitable friend for a nice Athenian boy!' Corinna said. Alexis looked uncomfortable. 'Oh, it's all right,' Corinna went on. 'I know that Athenian boys aren't supposed to be friendly with girls. And how is our friend Lucian?'

'Not very pleased with me,' said Alexis, trying to laugh. 'Sometimes I want to be on my own, but Lucian isn't like that. He wants to do things – sports, riding, swimming – every minute, and he wants me to do them too. And when I want an hour by myself, he thinks that I'm with *you*! That I *prefer* to be with you—'

'How stupid!' Corinna said.

16

'Yes,' Alexis agreed. 'But he won't believe me.'

People in the street were staring at them.

'We mustn't walk through the city together,' said Corinna. 'I don't want to make your father angry, and I want you and Lucian to be friends.'

'All right, but I shall be friends with you too.'

'Then come to the cave tomorrow. I'll give you a flute lesson!'

Ω Ω Ω

That afternoon Alexis found Lucian at the sports ground, and told him about Magnes and the statue. 'I had to talk to someone about it,' he said, 'and you're my best friend.'

This pleased Lucian, and he became more friendly. They walked home together, discussing the problem. 'I suppose,' Lucian said, 'that Hippias meant it was very dangerous for Magnes to be in Athens.'

'Could you tell *your* father that I think I saw Magnes? You needn't say how I know his face.'

'I've got a better idea,' said Lucian. 'I'll tell my uncle. He's on the City Council.'

As they were crossing the market-place, they saw Hippias standing with a group of men and boys.

'Perhaps we should keep an eye on Hippias,' said Lucian. 'If Magnes is planning something bad, Hippias is in it too. Let's go and listen.'

They joined the edge of the group, where the other boys were standing. Hippias was in the middle of the group, talking loudly about politics.

Hippias was talking loudly about politics.

'Democracy is a stupid idea,' he was saying. 'People just discuss things endlessly, and never decide anything. We often say that governing a country is like steering a ship. And can you have democracy on a ship? Do all the sailors discuss when to put up the sails, when to take them down, and who steers the ship? Everybody on the ship will soon be food for the fishes if that happens!'

There was some laughing in the group.

'Who *should* steer, Hippias?' Alexis could not see the

speaker, but it was the voice of a much older man. 'The man who has the most money on the ship?'

'He has the strongest reason to take care of it,' said Hippias.

'But is he the best man to steer?' the older man asked. 'Have you ever been in a storm at sea?'

'Of course! Many times.'

'And I suppose you always say to the poor sailor who is steering: "Give the wheel to the richest passenger. I'll feel much safer then." Is that what you say?'

Everybody laughed, but at Hippias this time, and his face went very red.

'Who is it?' Alexis whispered to Lucian. 'I must see.'

They moved round the edge of the group until they could see the speaker. 'Oh, it's Socrates,' said Lucian. 'That fat old man who walks the streets of Athens without shoes.'

Alexis knew his name and face. But it was the first time he had heard the voice which, people said, could work magic on those who heard it.

'Oh, we all know that you're the cleverest man in the world, Socrates!' said Hippias angrily.

'No, my young friend,' said the older man. 'I know nothing, but I *know* that I know nothing. Some people know nothing, but believe that they know everything.'

Hippias made an angry noise and walked away.

Socrates smiled at the others. 'Now you know why I'm sometimes called the Gadfly,' he said. 'I bite all animals, even well-born ones, and they run away across the fields!'

Alexis felt Lucian's hand on his arm. 'Come on.'

'Oh, all right,' said Alexis. But he had heard the magic voice of Socrates, and he wanted to stay.

Ω Ω Ω

Lucian spoke to his uncle, then reported back to Alexis. 'They don't think it was Magnes that you saw,' he said. 'They believe he's in Sparta, but they'll watch carefully for him now. Don't worry. The men on the Council know what they're doing.'

But Alexis wasn't so sure. He had begun to question the things that adults said and did. Although he believed that Athens was the finest city in Greece, he did not always agree with Athenian ideas. Why should Mother have supper in her own room when Father's friends came to visit? Women weren't stupid – why shouldn't they have intelligent conversations with men? He wanted to discuss questions like these, but he couldn't do it with Father, or with teachers like Milon.

He did not like Milon's lessons very much. Milon taught his students to make clever speeches – if the speeches were full of lies, it didn't matter. The important thing was to be clever. Alexis did not agree with this, and he found the ideas of Socrates both more honest and more interesting.

He did not tell his father, but several times he went to hear Socrates talking with his friends in the market-place. Socrates questioned everything. He did not argue; he just asked patient, simple questions to make people explain themselves. But the questions were like little knives, and the speakers often found themselves saying something very different from what they meant to say.

Alexis was interested in words and their meanings, and from Socrates and his friends he learnt new ways of thinking and discussing. He told Corinna all about them too. They met in the secret cave as often as they could. The flute lessons, and the lessons in reading and writing, went well, and they were now good friends.

But Alexis soon learnt that not everyone liked Socrates' ideas. One day he arrived home, and Theo told him, 'You're in trouble, Alex. Father's looking for you.'

Just then Father came in. 'Alexis,' he said, very seriously, 'I hear that you've been listening to Socrates in the market-

'You're in trouble, Alex, Father's looking for you.'

21

place. I don't want that clever old man filling your head with rubbish. Look at the kind of young man in his group – Plato! Xenophon! I don't want a son of mine talking to people like that! Socrates and his ideas are dangerous. Stay away from him!'

═ 4 ═

A PLAY IS BORN

Sons had to obey their fathers, of course, but Alexis was not happy about it.

'Never mind,' said Corinna, when Alexis told her about Father's order. She was lying on the floor of the cave, practising her writing. 'When you're famous because of your plays, you can talk to who you like.'

Alexis laughed. 'I've only written about two or three hundred lines of my tragedy.'

'But it's *good*,' said Corinna. 'I love that sad bit where Achilles learns that his best friend is dead. But why don't you write a comedy as well? You're good at jokes too.'

'You've got to have an idea first,' Alexis explained. 'You can't just sit down and begin to write.'

They stayed an hour or two at the cave that day, playing the flute and talking, and then began to walk home along the river valley. It was full summer now, and the fields around were turning to gold in the hot sun. They walked under the cool shadows of the trees.

Suddenly, Alexis stopped. 'Listen!' They heard men's voices in front of them. 'It sounds like Socrates,' Alexis said, 'but he doesn't go outside the city usually.'

Corinna looked through the trees. 'Then who is that lying on the grass over there? Come on, let's go and listen.'

'But Father said—'

'Your father won't worry if you hear nine or ten words,'

'Come on, let's go and listen.'

23

argued Corinna. 'Who are the others with Socrates?'

Alexis looked. 'Plato, Xenophon, and Phaedrus.'

They moved forward and hid behind some low trees. Suddenly, something came crashing through the trees, and Corinna screamed. It was only a friendly dog, but by then Xenophon had jumped to his feet and was pulling back the branches that hid them. It was too late to escape, so, with red faces, they stepped forward into the sunlight.

'Alexis!' said Socrates. He looked at Corinna, and smiled. 'So that's why you don't come to see us any more.'

'I haven't stopped him coming!' said Corinna.

'No? Perhaps it was your father, Alexis?'

Alexis felt uncomfortable. 'Father doesn't understand, I'm afraid. He thinks your ideas are dangerous.'

'You see?' Xenophon said to Socrates. 'You make enemies in the city. Some of us worry about you, Socrates. When people understand your ideas clearly, everything's fine. But hundreds don't, and writers make you look stupid in their plays, and audiences get the wrong ideas about you.' He turned to Plato. 'You're clever with words – why don't you write a comedy, and put the *real* Socrates in it? Something to explain his ideas and make him popular.'

Plato shook his head. 'I can't write comedies,' he said.

'Then do try to keep out of trouble, Socrates,' said Xenophon, 'and not make any more enemies.'

'I can't change my ways, Xenophon,' said Socrates. 'I am a gadfly – sent to bite Athenians, and make them think.'

Alexis and Corinna wanted to stay, but it was getting

late. So they said goodbye, and walked back to the city. Alexis was quiet.

'What are you thinking about?' asked Corinna.

'*The Gadfly*,' he said slowly. 'What a wonderful name for a comedy!'

Ω Ω Ω

The summer passed, and Alexis worked on his comedy. He realized that his tragedy about Achilles was not very good, but now, in *The Gadfly*, he felt that he had something important to say. He said it with jokes and songs, but the message was serious: 'This is the real Socrates. *He* isn't a danger to Athens, but other people are – those who lie, and cheat, and think too much of themselves.'

Only Corinna knew about the play. She listened to Alexis reading bits of it, she argued with him, and gave him ideas. Sometimes he worked in the cave, other times in Gorgo's warm, friendly kitchen. Those hours, and the hours when he was alone thinking of new ideas, were very happy ones.

Autumn came, and then winter. 'It'll be too cold to come here soon,' said Corinna. They were sitting in the cave's entrance, watching the rain. 'But then it will be spring, and the Theatre Festival. You must hurry and finish your play.'

'It *is* finished,' said Alexis. 'I wrote the final lines last night. Listen. It ends like this.'

Violet the crown of our city,
And sea-green the skirts of her robe!

Corinna was silent for a moment, then she said, 'It's

25

beautiful. It must be wonderful to be Athenian – to know that you really *belong* here. The audience will love it.'

'No audience will hear it,' said Alexis. 'The Festival Minister won't accept a play written by a boy.'

'But they *must* hear it, Alex! It's really good!'

And two days later Corinna was sure that she had the answer to the problem. She tried to catch Alexis on his way to Milon's house, but she met Lucian instead.

'I've got to see Alexis,' she said. 'Will you tell him?'

Lucian did not look pleased to see her. 'All right, I'll tell him. I – I have to go now. I'm late.'

'I hear that you are the best cook in Athens.'

Corinna went back to the inn and watched for Alexis while she did some work for Gorgo in the kitchen. People came and went, and later in the morning a very grand young gentleman, in an expensive cloak and boots, arrived.

'I'm giving a special supper party,' he said to Gorgo, 'and I hear that you are the best cook in Athens.'

Gorgo smiled. 'Very kind of you to say so, sir.'

'I want the best of everything. Can you get somebody to do the music, some dancing, that kind of thing?'

'Yes, sir,' said Gorgo. 'I can get you some of the best in the business – nice girls, too.'

'Pretty faces aren't everything,' he said. 'There was a flute-girl at one of my parties. Pretty as a picture, but she couldn't play the flute.' He saw Corinna in the corner. 'Is she one of your girls?'

'My own daughter, sir. *She* plays the flute wonderfully' – Gorgo stopped when she saw Corinna's angry face, then went on – 'but she's too young for parties.'

'What a pity,' said the young man. He gave Gorgo the date of the party, and the number of people coming.

'And what is your name, sir?' asked Gorgo.

At that moment Alexis appeared in the doorway.

'Hippias,' the young man said. The doorway was behind him so he did not see Alexis, who quickly went out again.

Hippias left, and Gorgo turned to Corinna. 'People will pay you good money to play that flute at parties,' she said. 'Some mothers *make* their girls go!'

Corinna did not answer. Oh, how she hated the inn!

27

She knew the money was needed, but she didn't want to be a flute-girl, playing at parties where men drank too much and became too friendly. 'I wish I had a father!' she thought.

Gorgo never spoke about him, only to say that he had died when Corinna was a baby. Corinna once asked if she ever had any brothers or sisters, and Gorgo said no. But years later Corinna heard her say to a neighbour, 'When my little boy was born . . .' Corinna questioned Gorgo afterwards. 'He died,' Gorgo said. 'I only had him for a day or two, so I don't talk about him.'

'We need friends like Hippias,' Gorgo was saying now. 'We're foreigners, remember. The Athenians can throw us out of their city at any time. Hippias will be a useful friend – more useful than that boy! *His* father doesn't give big parties.'

'Oh, be quiet, Mum!' cried Corinna. Alexis was coming back in, smiling all over his face. Gorgo looked at him and, without a word, went back to her kitchen.

'Hippias didn't see me, luckily,' Alexis told Corinna. 'Lucian said you wanted me.'

'Yes,' she said. 'I've been asking questions. Do you know how old Aristophanes was when he put on his first play? No older than you! He sent it in with another person's name on it. He had a friend who was an actor—'

'But I don't know any actors.'

'It doesn't matter. Ask any adult. Perhaps one of your father's friends . . .'

28

'I'm not going to ask Father!' Alexis said. He thought hard. 'Yes, I've got it! Uncle Paintbrush!'

Ω Ω Ω

Uncle Paintbrush was really Great-uncle Alexis, Father's uncle, but the children always called him Uncle Paintbrush because he was a vase-painter. He was getting old now, and a little forgetful, but he was a kind, gentle man.

He was busy working on a black and red vase when Alexis arrived at his workroom that evening. While Alexis explained his problem, Uncle Paintbrush listened, and watched Alexis with friendly blue eyes.

Uncle Paintbrush watched him with friendly blue eyes.

'So will you let me send the play in under your name?' asked Alexis. 'It's really very suitable, because *your* name is Alexis, son of Leon – just like mine. And you needn't worry. There's not one chance in a hundred that the play will win a place in the Festival.'

'Well . . . all right, then,' said Uncle Paintbrush.

═ 5 ═

UNCLE PAINTBRUSH IN TROUBLE

Eight days later, just as Alexis and his family were finishing dinner, Uncle Paintbrush arrived. He looked worried.

'Can I speak to Alexis – outside, please?' he said.

'What has the boy done now?' asked Father crossly.

'Nothing at all, Leon. I – I want him to help me. A little problem, that's all. Can I have him for the afternoon?'

Outside, Alexis said, 'What is it, Uncle? Is it the play? Where are we going?'

'To see the Minister! He wants to see me about *my* play! But I didn't write it – I haven't even *read* it!'

Ω Ω Ω

The Minister was an old man, with a smile in his eyes.

'Alexis, son of Leon?' he asked.

'Yes, Minister,' replied Uncle Paintbrush.

'Sit down, then,' said the Minister. 'Who is the boy?'

'My nephew. He – he helps me.'

'Your play reads like the work of a twenty-year-old,'

30

said the Minister, 'so I thought I'd see someone younger.'

'A man is as old as he feels, Minister.'

'Yes, indeed. But there are a few problems, perhaps. How are you going to get a cow on the stage?'

'A *cow*?' repeated Uncle Paintbrush, surprised.

'You remember, Uncle,' Alexis said quickly, 'when the gadfly bites the cow, and the cow jumps up and down.' He turned to the Minister. 'Uncle wants to use two men inside a big skin – the front one with a cow's head, and the back one with a tail.'

'Mmm. Do you think it will work?' said the Minister.

'Why not, sir?' said Alexis quickly. 'Someone used a horse the year before last – *that* was two men in a skin.'

The Minister gave Alexis a long look. 'Did they?'

Alexis tried to keep calm. Did this man believe them?

'Another difficult thing,' said the Minister, after a moment, 'is the entrance of the Egyptian.'

'Oh . . . well . . .' began Uncle Paintbrush. 'Of course—'

'The Minister is thinking of *another* play, isn't he, Uncle?' said Alexis, his eyes full of warning. 'There *isn't* an Egyptian in yours, is there?'

'Of course not,' said Uncle Paintbrush crossly.

'My mistake,' the Minister said politely. He stared hard at Alexis. 'You know the play almost as well as your uncle.'

'I – I wrote most of it down for him, sir. His eyes aren't as good as they used to be.'

'I see. There were other questions I wanted to ask, but perhaps it's better if I don't. It doesn't matter to me if a

31

writer is as old as the hills, or—' here he gave Alexis a half-smile '—as young as you like. But Athenian audiences don't always think like that.'

'Does that mean, sir,' asked Alexis, 'that – that the play is no good . . . that it hasn't won a place?'

'No, my boy. It's a good play. I know no reason why it should not have a place in the Festival – and I don't *want* to know a reason.' He looked at Uncle Paintbrush. 'We will tell you later the name of the man who will pay the costs of putting on the play. You will produce it—'

'Me?' said Uncle Paintbrush, looking frightened. 'But—'

'I'm sure your nephew will be a great help,' said the

'I'm sure your nephew will be a great help,' said the Minister pleasantly.

32

Minister pleasantly. 'He will be able to remember all the things that you yourself forget. Good luck, sir.'

Ω Ω Ω

'This is terrible!' said Uncle Paintbrush as they hurried home. Alexis was almost dancing with happiness. 'I don't know *anything* about plays. What are we going to do?'

'Produce the play!' said Alexis. 'I'll tell you what to say to the actors. You just have to say it.'

At home they told the family the news, still pretending, of course, that it was Uncle Paintbrush's play.

'Clever Uncle Paintbrush!' Theo shouted.

'*I* shan't be able to see it,' said Nico crossly.

Uncle Paintbrush asked for Alexis' help with the play. This meant missing lessons, but Father could not easily refuse. It was a great thing for the family, to have a play in the Festival, and everyone was very pleased and excited.

Later Alexis ran to the inn to tell Corinna the news.

'Oh, Alexis! How wonderful!' she cried.

It was always a rich Athenian who had to pay the costs of a Festival play, and the next day they heard that a man named Conon was going to pay for *The Gadfly*. 'He has a farm out beyond Colonus,' said Uncle Paintbrush. 'He lives very simply, but he has plenty of money.'

That afternoon Alexis and Uncle Paintbrush walked to the farm in the winter sunshine. They met Conon outside the farmhouse and explained who they were.

'Yes, the Minister sent me a message,' said Conon. He was not as old as Uncle Paintbrush, but had a deeply lined, unhappy face. 'How much money do you want?'

'How much can we have, sir?' said Alexis, hopefully.

Conon looked at him. 'And who are you?' he said.

'This is my nephew,' said Uncle Paintbrush. 'He's helping me with the play, because I'm a bit forgetful.'

'Then you're lucky,' said Conon. 'Some things are best forgotten.' He was silent for a moment, then went on, 'Well, come into the house and we'll discuss things.'

He took them into a living-room, where a grey-haired woman immediately stood up and began to leave.

'No need to go, my dear,' Conon said gently. 'My wife, Demetria,' he said to his visitors. 'We don't follow the

'No need to go, my dear,' Conon said gently.

34

ways of the city here. I will never understand why the woman of the house must run out of her own living-room every time her husband brings a visitor home.'

His wife fetched some drinks and cakes, and sat down again. 'How old are you?' she asked Alexis. He told her. 'Really? Our own child was nearly the same—'

'Our visitors have come to talk about the Festival,' Conon said quickly. 'Now, tell me what is needed.'

Alexis told him and for a while they discussed the play. In the end Conon said, 'I'll tell my banker that you can have as much money as you need. And just ask me if you want any more. The boy can come out here with messages.' He smiled kindly at Alexis.

When they had left and were walking home, Alexis said, 'He's a nice man, although he seemed a bit cold at first.'

'I remember something about Conon now,' said Uncle Paintbrush. 'He married a woman as old as himself, instead of the usual young girl. They had a son, who died. And by then his wife was too old to have any more children.'

Alexis remembered Conon's unhappy face, and his wife's soft, gentle voice. 'How sad,' he said.

Ω Ω Ω

Work on producing the play began immediately, and life became very busy for Alexis. The chief actor, Glaucus, was difficult at first, and Alexis still had to pretend that all the orders came from Uncle Paintbrush, although they were really his own. There was very little time to see Corinna, but ten days before the Festival they managed to meet

35

outside the city and go up to the cave. There had been snow the day before and it was very cold.

When they reached the cave, Alexis said, 'Look! Someone's been here. There are footprints in the snow.'

'One man,' said Corinna. 'He made a fire, too!'

'What's this?' said Alexis. He picked up a long thin piece of half-burned cloth. 'There's writing on it.'

Corinna read the letters. 'FPABEEEPILR—' She stopped. 'It doesn't *mean* anything.'

'Yes, it does,' said Alexis. 'It's a stick-message!'

═══ 6 ═══

A MESSAGE FROM THE ENEMY

'It's the Spartan way of sending secret messages,' Alexis explained. 'They put a cloth round and round a stick, then they write the message *along* it. And when you take the cloth off the stick, you just get a lot of letters, like this.'

'And you can only read it if you put it round the same stick again!' said Corinna.

'Yes, the same stick, or one the same thickness.'

'But we don't know how thick the stick was.' She looked at the cloth in her hand, and at the letters.

FPABEEEPILREAHOPNAEMTOFIANTATUHALSODHSIS

'I wish we could read the message!' she said.

'But I think we can,' said Alexis. He picked up a stick. 'How many letters does it take to go once round this stick?

'Someone's been here. There are footprints in the snow.'

Seven. So if *this* was the stick, the eighth letter would follow the first, and then the fifteenth . . .'

'FPO . . . I don't think so!' said Corinna.

'So, seven isn't right. And with letters as big as this, it won't be two, three, or four—'

'Because it would be an impossibly thin stick.'

'Right. So more than five, but probably less than twelve. And we know it isn't every seventh letter. You try below seven, and I'll try above seven, until the message says something sensible.'

They held the piece of cloth between them, staring at

the letters. Almost immediately Alexis shouted, 'It's eight!
Look!' He took a stick and wrote the letters on the ground.

F	P	A	B	E	E	E	P
I	L	R	E	A	H	O	P
N	A	E	M	T	O	F	I
A	N	T	A	T	U	H	A
L	S	O	D	H	S	I	S

'Hippias!' Corinna cried.

'Yes,' Alexis said, reading downwards: '*Final plans are
to be made at the house of Hippias.*'

'Plans for what?' said Corinna.

'Do you remember,' Alexis said, 'the man that I saw at
the torch race – Magnes? He was in Sparta, and this is a
Spartan stick-message. I think the man who used the cave
was either Magnes or someone passing a message between
him and Hippias. I don't like the sound of "final plans".
They must be getting ready to do something very bad.'

'A revolution?'

'Magnes has tried it before. And if he wants to throw
out the Council and govern Athens himself, the Spartans
will be happy to help. They don't like our democracy at
all.' He looked at the cloth. 'But this isn't enough. We
need some real information before we tell the Council.'

'If there's anything more to discover, it will be at
Hippias' house,' said Corinna. 'He's giving a big party
next week, a few days before the Festival. Perhaps that's
when he and his friends will make their final plans.'

'Yes!' Alexis said. 'I'll get into the house and hide—'

'Don't be stupid, Alex. Do you *want* a knife in your back? They'll watch every man who goes into the house. But they won't worry about the poor stupid *girls*, who are only there to dance and sing – and play the flute.'

'*What?*' cried Alexis. 'You mean you'll go as a flute-girl? You can't do that!'

'Don't look so worried.' Corinna laughed. 'I can take care of myself. And Mum will be pleased!'

Ω Ω Ω

These were brave words, but when the night of the party arrived, Corinna felt less sure of herself. The meal went well, as it always did with Gorgo's cooking, and Hippias looked pleased. Then the drinking started and the dancers were called in. Corinna followed them.

The flute was not needed all the time, and as the evening went on she was able to watch Hippias. He went from group to group, speaking to two or three men, then moving on. Corinna was sure that he was discussing the plans for the revolution. She tried hard to listen, but only once heard something which sounded important.

' . . . Hippias will ask him that when they meet.'

'Yes, but when will they meet?'

'The night before the Festival. It's dangerous for him to come into the city, so Hippias is going out to meet him.'

A third voice said, 'I'm still not happy about the Council. If they—'

'Don't worry about them. We've got the answer. Hippias told us. In his wife's room!'

There was a lot of laughing which Corinna could not understand. Then she remembered. Hippias was not married. So what did it mean?

She tried to hear more but then Hippias himself came and put his arm round her. 'The little flute-girl!' he said. 'You played well. Come and sit with me later, and we'll talk.'

Corinna wanted to go home. She had picked up only one piece of information: Hippias was meeting someone, probably Magnes, outside Athens on the night before the Festival. It wasn't much, for an unpleasant evening's work. But what about this 'wife's room', where the 'answer' was? Perhaps she could find it . . .

When Hippias moved away, she went quietly out of the room. She took her shoes in her hand and went upstairs to the family bedrooms. One room seemed bigger than the others, and she tried to open the door – but it was locked.

'Who's that?' said a voice from the stairs.

Corinna turned quickly. More stairs went up into the darkness, and she ran up them. The sound of feet followed her. A moment later, she was on the flat roof. There were stars in the sky, but no moon.

'Come here, you young thief!' shouted the man.

Corinna ran across the roof to the far side, and saw that there was a tall tree close to the wall of the house. She dropped her shoes and flute over the side of the roof, and jumped wildly into the tree. She half-fell, half-climbed, and finally crashed to the ground.

40

Corinna jumped wildly into the tree.

Someone jumped from the shadows and helped her up.
'Are you all right?' said a well-known voice.
'Alex!' she cried.
'I've been here all evening,' he said. 'I hated the idea of
you in that house. Come on, let's get away from here.'

Ω Ω Ω

They talked more calmly the next morning.
'They're planning *something*,' said Corinna.
'Who will believe us?' said Alexis. 'What have we got?

41

A piece of cloth, and bits of conversation that you heard. Did they say Magnes' name? No.'

'You saw him at the torch race! With Hippias!'

'That was months ago. And nobody really believed me.'

'What about the locked bedroom?' said Corinna.

'Hippias will say that it's locked because it isn't used. If someone wants to search it, Hippias will get a warning from his friends. There are five hundred men on the Council, remember; I'm sure Hippias has some friends among them.'

'Didn't I do *anything* useful last night?' Corinna said.

'Of course you did,' said Alexis. 'We know Hippias is meeting someone in four days' time. I'll follow him and—'

'I'll come with you,' said Corinna.

'No, you won't!' he said. 'It's my turn to do something now, and I'll do it better alone.'

=== 7 ===

A NIGHT FOR SPYING

Hippias' house was in a busy street, and was easy to watch. Alexis made his face dirty, and put on an old coat, big boots, and a hat. Then he sat in a doorway, like a farm boy who was resting before the long walk back to his village. The afternoon passed. Lights came on. At last, Hippias and two slaves came out, and Alexis began to follow them. At first there were plenty of people going along the road to the eastern hills. Then the crowd became thinner and when the moon came up, shining with a bright silvery light, Alexis had to stay in the shadows of the trees.

They went towards the river, and soon Alexis recognized the trees and the rocks. They were going to the cave!

As they got nearer, Hippias called out and a man answered. It sounded like a Spartan's voice.

'Your slaves must wait here and help the others to keep watch. Magnes is in the cave.'

Hippias and the other man went towards the cave, and Alexis followed, going round to the right to get past the group of slaves. There was a fire in the cave entrance. He saw two shadows, and heard a new voice speak.

Then Hippias said, 'You'll sleep in a more comfortable bed tomorrow night, sir, I can promise you.'

'We won't sleep much tomorrow night,' Magnes said. 'But the night *after*, we can – if all goes well. You've met my good friend, Callibius, of Sparta . . .'

The three men moved into the cave, and Alexis had to climb the tree to hear and see them round the fire.

'Everything is ready for tomorrow night,' Hippias said. 'After the Festival plays finish, there is a carnival. Everyone wears masks and carnival clothes. We will too, and so nobody will recognize Magnes. We can hide our knives under our cloaks. I've got two hundred long knives—'

'Where?' asked Callibius.

'Locked in the large bedroom in my house.'

'The Council chiefs will be killed during the carnival,'

Magnes said. 'We must make people believe that there are more of us than there are. So when the rest of the Council meet early the next morning, they'll be frightened. They'll wonder what's going to happen next. And it'll be easy for one of my friends on the Council to say, "Bring back Magnes! He's the only man who can save the country!"'

Alexis' blood went cold. He must get back to Athens at once, to warn the Council. He climbed down the tree . . . and into the strong arms that were waiting to catch him.

The men in the cave above heard the noise. 'Who is it?' Magnes called down. 'Who have you got there?'

'He looks like a farm boy, sir, from his clothes,' said the slave. 'He was in the tree, spying.'

'He isn't a farm boy!' said Hippias, staring down. 'He's Alexis, son of Leon. I've seen him with Socrates.'

'Well, Alexis,' said Magnes, 'who sent you to spy on us?'

'Nobody,' said Alexis. 'My father's farm is near here. I often go there, and I like walking in the dark. I saw the fire and wondered what it was. I've only been here a minute—'

'He's lying,' said Callibius. 'He's dangerous. Probably heard everything we said. There's only one thing to do—'

'No,' said Magnes. 'We only kill when we must.'

They brought Alexis up to the cave and tied his hands and legs. 'Don't try to escape, or do anything stupid,' Magnes said to him. 'You can stay here until tomorrow night and go home safely when all this is finished.'

'Don't try to escape,' Magnes said.

After a while Hippias left, and the other two went to
sleep in the narrow cave entrance. Alexis lay at the back
of the cave, helpless and hopeless. Towards morning he
fell asleep, and dreamed he was in the theatre, trying to
warn the audience. And when he began to wake up, the
words in his dream were still running through his head.

Men of Athens, brave and free, now hear this warning!
Lock the gates, or you'll be slaves before the morning!

45

You need not fear a writer's jokes, but watch for danger
In party masks, from long-nosed men, from friend and
   stranger!
Enemies all, beneath their cloaks they hide long knives,
At night they'll come – to steal your city and take your
   lives!

'Alexis! Alexis!'

Alexis opened his eyes. Someone was saying his name.

Ω   Ω   Ω

When Alexis had followed Magnes to the cave, someone had followed *him*. It was Corinna. She hid behind some rocks and watched as Alexis was caught and taken into the cave. Then she ran back to the city, to Lucian's house.

It was just beginning to get light, and people were already getting up because of the Festival. Lucian came to the door, looking sleepy. He did not look pleased to see Corinna.

'I know you don't like me,' Corinna said, 'but Alexis is in danger.' She told him what had happened.

'I'll tell my father,' Lucian said at once. 'We'll get some men together, and—'

'No. That will be very dangerous for Alexis,' she said. 'They'll probably do – do something terrible to him.'

'You're right. But can we get him out on our own?'

'I think we can. Listen.' When she explained her plan, Lucian looked surprised. 'But I need your help,' she said.

'Of course, yes. I'm pleased you came for me.'

And they hurried out of the city.

Ω   Ω   Ω

'Alexis! Alexis!' Corinna whispered in his ear. He turned and saw her. 'Don't make a sound.'

She had already untied his legs, and was now working on his hands. After a moment, they were free, and she helped him to stand up. He could not see Magnes or Callibius, but he could hear their voices just outside the cave.

'How did you get past them?' Alexis whispered. 'Now we're *both* in danger! We can't get out!'

'Come on – quickly!' she said. 'This way.' She pulled him into the darkness at the back of the cave.

'But they'll just search and find us,' he said.

'They won't find us. Keep close behind me.'

So he followed her – a shadow, climbing, moving up, until she was a black shape against a circle of blue sky. Then they were out on the top of a hill, with mountains standing around them in the early morning sun.

'You never told me there was another way out of the cave!' Alexis said.

'It was my special secret. I wasn't sure that I was going to like you, or Lucian.' She looked down the side of the hill. 'He's down there now, somewhere in the trees.'

'*Lucian?*'

'He went crashing around by the river, to bring them out of the cave to look. Don't worry, they won't catch Lucian.'

'No,' said Alexis. 'And we must get back to the city as fast as we can. Today's the day for the revolution!'

═ 8 ═

THE FESTIVAL AT LAST

The Festival had already started when they reached the dressing-rooms behind the stage.

'At last! You've come!' cried Uncle Paintbrush.

'We were afraid something had happened to you,' said a calm, kindly voice. Alexis turned to see Conon smiling at him. 'But why are you wearing a farm boy's clothes? And this young lady . . .' He stared at Corinna. 'Who . . . How – how did you get here?'

'I know women don't come into the theatre,' said Corinna, 'but there's a special reason today.'

'I'm sure there is, young lady, but—'

'Please, sir,' Alexis said. He had to get news to the Council quickly, and Conon was the best person to take it. Everybody that Alexis knew was lost somewhere in the audience, and Uncle Paintbrush was too worried about the play to think straight. 'I must talk to you,' Alexis said to Conon. And in a low voice, he told his story.

Conon listened. 'This is terrible,' he said. 'We must tell the army generals – they're all sitting out there in the audience, but I can get to one of them when this first play finishes. I'll bring him round here.'

Alexis found a clean tunic in the dressing-room cupboard, and put it on. Corinna picked up his farm boy's clothes. 'I must go. People are giving me angry looks.'

'At last! You've come!' cried Uncle Paintbrush.

'Where can I find you when it's all finished?'

'At home, where all good girls should be,' she replied. 'Conon called me "young lady", did you hear? I think he's nice. Goodbye, Alex, and good luck!'

After the first play Alexis went to meet Conon and the general. The general asked him several questions, then said, 'You've done well, young man. But we must act quickly – and we need more names.' Alexis had given him the names of Hippias and a few others that Corinna had recognized at the supper party. 'We can arrest these men after the Festival,' the general said, 'but what will the others do?'

'Perhaps they won't do anything tonight,' said Alexis.

'Then they'll hide and try to fight another day. We need to know who they are, and we need to get them now!'

49

'I've got an idea!' said Alexis suddenly. 'Hippias doesn't know that I've escaped. Magnes may send someone to warn him, but how will he find Hippias in that crowd out there? But suppose Hippias *does* get a warning that everything is discovered. Will he go on sitting there, enjoying the play?'

'No, he'll get out as fast as he can!' said Conon.

'And his friends – *all* of them – will do the same when they see Hippias hurrying out of the theatre.'

'But we can't shout "Everything is discovered" in the middle of a Festival play!' said the general.

Alexis' eyes were shining. 'We give the warning from the stage, sir! The rest of the audience will know nothing about it. *You* put soldiers at every exit to arrest every man who walks out during my play. *I'll* write the words that will send Hippias and his friends running for the city gates!'

Ω Ω Ω

Alexis was probably the only person who did not enjoy the first half of *The Gadfly*. He was

50

waiting for the long speech by Glaucus, the chief actor, in the middle of the play. Glaucus had learnt his six new lines, which were the words Alexis remembered from his dream in the cave. They were not great lines, but the warning was clear enough.

He climbed up on to the roof of the dressing-rooms to watch. Below him, he could see the thousands of people in the audience. And somewhere among that great crowd were Hippias and his friends.

At last the moment came. Glaucus stepped forward and began his speech. First came the jokes, some of them about

Glaucus stepped forward and began his speech.

Socrates, and the audience shook with laughter. Good old
Socrates! *He* wasn't a danger to Athens . . . Then Glaucus
spoke more seriously. He warned Athenians of dangers
that were coming, and the audience became silent and still
as Glaucus came to the last lines of his speech:

Men of Athens, brave and free, now hear this warning!
Lock the gates, or you'll be slaves before the morning!
You need not fear a writer's jokes, but watch for danger
In party masks, from long-nosed men, from friend and
stranger!
Enemies all, beneath their cloaks they hide long knives,
At night they'll come – to steal your city and take your
lives!

For a moment the audience was silent, not sure what to
do. Then the funny cow ran on to the stage, and everyone
began to laugh loudly.

But some people did not stay to watch the cow.

Alexis saw small groups of men getting up and pushing
their way through the crowd to the exits. They seemed to
be in a hurry, and Alexis smiled. Athens was safe.

A little later Lucian found him on the roof. 'Alexis,
they've got soldiers all round the theatre!' he whispered.

'I know,' Alexis whispered back. 'But can you just shut
up while I listen to the rest of my play.'

'*Your* play?' said Lucian, staring at him. He lay down
on the roof next to his friend, and watched the stage.

Violet the crown of our city,
And sea-green the skirts of her robe.

The play came to an end, and there was a moment when everyone was silent. Then came a storm of shouting and clapping, filling the theatre with noise and telling Alexis that *The Gadfly* was a great success.

After a while the audience became quiet again as they waited for the name of the winning play in that year's Festival. And at last the answer came . . .

'*The Gadfly*, by Alexis, son of Leon.'

Ω Ω Ω

Soon everyone knew just which Alexis, son of Leon, had written the play, and Conon decided to give a party. 'A friend has said that I can use his town-house,' he said to Alexis. 'But can we get a cook?'

'I think I can find you one, sir,' said Alexis.

Conon laughed. 'I'm sure you can! I now know that you wrote your uncle's play *and* stopped a revolution, so I'm sure you can do a little thing like finding me a cook!'

'I had a lot of help from Corinna.'

'That young lady I saw at the stage-door?'

'Yes, sir. And her mother is a cook.'

'Get her, then, my boy. Ask her to plan for fifty. There's thirty actors, your family, your friend Lucian, and – anybody *you* want to ask.'

'Can I invite Socrates?' asked Alexis.

'Of course,' said Conon. 'Tell my slave where to find him, then go and get that cook. What's her name?'

'Gorgo, sir.'

'Gorgo? I've heard that name before. But where? I

haven't been to a party for years.' Conon turned to his slave. 'When you've invited Socrates, run home and ask my wife to come to the party. Tell her that there'll be no heavy drinking, no flute-girls or anything of that kind—'

'Sir,' said Alexis, 'we must have *one* flute-girl, or the cook won't come – and neither will I!'

Ω Ω Ω

Alexis ran to the inn, and Corinna came running out of the kitchen to meet him. 'Oh, Alex, well done!' she cried.

'You've heard the news, then?' said Alexis.

'Heard?' she laughed. 'I *saw* it!' She showed him his farm boy's clothes, which were lying on the floor. 'You can have your smelly old clothes back. They were very useful in the theatre. Nobody wanted to sit too near me!'

'You mean . . .?' Alexis began to laugh.

Gorgo came to the kitchen door. 'What's happening?'

'I've got a job for you,' said Alexis. 'Tonight. Dinner for fifty. The best of everything!'

Ω Ω Ω

It was the happiest evening of Alexis' life.

Father arrived, and put his arms round Alexis. 'Is it true what they're saying all round the city? That *you* wrote the play, not Uncle Alexis? Oh, well done, my boy!'

Socrates was a great success with Father. After *The Gadfly*, Father no longer seemed to think that Socrates' ideas were dangerous.

But the great moment came when Corinna entered, in a long blue-grey dress that was the same colour as her eyes.

54

She carried her flute in her hand, and wore an old silver brooch in the shape of a grasshopper.

As she played, Conon walked quietly into the next room where his wife, Alexis' mother, and Nico were watching.

'What a pretty girl,' said Demetria, smiling.

'Who does she look like, do you think, my dear?' Conon's voice sounded strange.

Demetria looked. 'Nobody that I can remember.'

'That's not surprising. It was . . . some time ago. And you only saw the other girl in your mirror.'

Demetria stared at him. 'What do you mean, Conon?'

'She looks just like you, when you were younger.'

'How strange,' said Demetria.

'She looks just like you, when you were younger.'

'I thought so, until I asked her mother's name,' said Conon. 'It's Gorgo.'

Demetria's face went white. 'If it is, there's nothing we can do,' she whispered. 'We did wrong, and we must pay for it. The girl is happy as she is.'

'She's not,' said Conon. 'And Gorgo isn't happy. Oh, they like each other, but the child does not enjoy her life.'

'You've spoken to both of them?'

'Gorgo, yes. But not Corinna. I wanted to tell you first.'

'Oh, bring her now, Conon!' And as Corinna finished playing and came through the doorway, Demetria said, 'Look, she still has my silver grasshopper brooch!'

Corinna stood white and silent while Conon and Demetria explained. They had married for love, against the wishes of their families. For years they had no child, and then a baby was born – not the son that Conon wanted so much, but a girl. There was no chance of another child, so they did what rich families often did. They paid a woman to give them her baby son, and take their daughter instead. Gorgo needed the money, she was leaving Athens, and she thought a daughter would be more useful to her.

'Your mother didn't want to do it,' Conon said. 'It was *my* idea. But I realized later that I almost broke her heart.'

Corinna remembered what Alexis had told her about Conon, and the son who had died. So that was really Gorgo's boy! Perhaps Conon had done wrong by sending his own daughter away, but he had paid for it in the sadness of the boy's death. 'So *that* was what Gorgo meant tonight in the kitchen,' she thought.

'You'll never be happy in this life,' Gorgo had said. 'And I only want you to be happy. But we'll always be good friends, won't we?'

So Gorgo knew. And she didn't mind. Corinna put her arms round her father, and then turned and threw herself into Demetria's arms . . .

Hours later, when the party was almost finished, Alexis and Corinna stood in the street, enjoying the cool air. 'So you're going to be an Athenian young lady!' said Alexis, laughing. 'How are you going to like that?'

'We'll live on the farm, and a girl is freer in the country,' she said. 'I shan't run upstairs every time you come!'

'How do you know I'll come? It's a long walk.'

She smiled but did not answer. For a few moments they stood silent in the street. Suddenly the sky lit up with the early morning sun, and they saw the Acropolis hill, with its soft violet shadows – the city's crown of violet.

Corinna put her arm through his. 'You know, Alex,' she said, 'it's wonderful, in all kinds of ways, to know that I'm an Athenian!'

GLOSSARY

audience a group of people listening to a play, a speaker, etc.

carnival a big party, when people come together in the streets
for dancing, singing, playing music, etc.

council a group of people who are chosen to work together to
decide things for other people

crown a kind of 'hat' usually worn by a king or queen

democracy the kind of government in which people choose the
men and women who govern or lead them

festival a time when many people come together to see plays,
listen to music, etc.

gadfly a kind of fly which bites cows and horses

general *(n)* an important officer in the army

govern to make the laws and rules in a country

inn a house where you can buy food and drink

joke *(n)* something that you say to make people laugh

magic making wonderful or impossible things happen

minister an important person in the government

politics the work of government

practise to do something often until you are good at it

produce to plan and control the way a play is acted

public speaking speaking to large groups of people

race *(n)* a competition to see who can run, ride, etc. the fastest

revolution a sudden change in the way a country is governed

robe a long, loose piece of clothing

sculptor someone who makes statues from stone, wood, etc.

slave someone who is owned by another person and who
receives no money for their work

Spartan a person from the Greek city of Sparta

steer to turn a wheel to guide a boat, ship, etc.

team a group of people who play a sport together

violet a soft blue-purple colour; also a flower of that colour

Before Reading

1 **Read the story introduction on the first page of the book, and the back cover. How much do you know now about the story? Are these sentences true (T) or false (F)?**

1 This story happens in Greece a long time ago. T/F

2 Alexis and Corinna write a play together. T/F

3 Corinna is not from Athens. T/F

4 Boys have more fun than girls in Athens. T/F

5 People are planning a revolution to bring democracy to Athens. T/F

2 **What will happen in the story? Can you guess? Choose words to complete each sentence.**

1 The revolution *will* / *will not* succeed.

2 Alexis and his friends will *stop* / *help* the revolution.

3 Alexis' play *will* / *will not* be accepted for the Festival.

4 Corinna and Alexis will *stay friends* / *become enemies*.

3 **Why is the Acropolis hill in Athens called the 'crown of violet'? Can you guess? Choose one of these answers.**

1 Because the hill is high above the city.

2 Because the King lives there.

3 Because the rocks are the colour of a violet.

4 Because the hill is covered in violet flowers.

ACTIVITIES

While Reading

Read Chapters 1 to 3. Choose the best question-word for these questions, and then answer them.

What / Where / Who / Why

1 . . . did Alexis go with his family?
2 . . . wanted to sit in Leon's seat?
3 . . . had to leave the theatre when the comedies began?
4 . . . was Corinna born?
5 . . . did Corinna hate Athens?
6 . . . did Alexis and Corinna agree to teach each other?
7 . . . did the riders have to carry in the relay race?
8 . . . was unusual about the stranger with Hippias?
9 . . . was Alexis angry with Lucian?
10 . . . did Alexis and Lucian decide to do about Magnes?
11 . . . said that democracy was a stupid idea?
12 . . . was special about Socrates's voice?
13 . . . did Alexis prefer Socrates to Milon?
14 . . . did Alexis and Corinna meet for their lessons?
15 . . . did Alexis' father, Leon, think of Socrates?

Before you read Chapter 4 (*A play is born*), can you guess what happens? Choose words to complete these sentences.

1 Alexis writes a second play, which is a *comedy / tragedy*.
2 It is about *Magnes / Socrates* and his *revolution / ideas*.
3 At first only *Lucian / Corinna* knows about Alexis' play.

61

Read Chapters 4 and 5. Who said this, and to whom? Who, or what, were they talking about?

1 'He thinks your ideas are dangerous.'
2 'It's beautiful . . . The audience will love it.'
3 'I want the best of everything.'
4 '*His* father doesn't give big parties.'
5 'Will you let me send the play in under your name?'
6 'But I didn't write it – I haven't even read it!'
7 'You know the play almost as well as your uncle.'
8 'He lives very simply, but he has plenty of money.'
9 'Our own child was nearly the same—'
10 'Someone's been here. There are footprints in the snow.'

Before you read Chapter 6, can you guess who the stick-message is for?

1 the City Council
2 Socrates and his friends
3 the enemies of Athens
4 Alexis and Corinna

Read Chapters 6 and 7. Are these sentences true (T) or false (F)? Rewrite the false ones with the correct information.

1 Corinna said she would go to Hippias' party as a flute-girl.
2 At the party Corinna picked up a lot of information.
3 When someone chased Corinna up the stairs, she climbed out of a window.
4 Alexis dressed like a farm boy when he followed Hippias.
5 Magnes, Hippias and the others were planning to kill the Council chiefs with heavy stones during the carnival.

6 Magnes wanted to kill Alexis but Callibius didn't agree.

7 Lucian had followed Alexis to the cave.

8 Corinna knew a secret way out of the back of the cave.

Before you read Chapter 8, can you guess how the story ends? Choose Y (yes) or N (no) for each sentence.

1 Hippias and his friends will be arrested. Y/N

2 Alexis' play will win. Y/N

3 Leon will give a big party. Y/N

4 Corinna will find her father. Y/N

Read Chapter 8, and put these sentences in the right order.

1 The soldiers arrested everybody who left the theatre during the play.

2 From the stage Glaucus spoke the lines which warned the people of Athens that their democracy was in danger.

3 Conon gave a big party for everyone after the play.

4 Alexis wrote new lines for the play and Glaucus learned them.

5 Alexis told first Conon, then the army general about the plans for the revolution.

6 The winning play in the festival was *The Gadfly*.

7 Hippias and his friends left the theatre in a hurry.

8 Corinna discovered that Conon and Demetria were her real mother and father, and that she was an Athenian.

9 At the same time the general sent soldiers to every exit of the theatre.

After Reading

1 Corinna is telling Lucian about her plan to get Alexis out of the cave. Put their conversation in the right order and write in the speakers' names. Corinna speaks first (number 3).

1 _____ 'No, it won't. The men will probably be in the cave with Alexis so I won't be able to get near him.'

2 _____ 'Right! Then the men will come out to find out what's happening—'

3 _____ 'Listen, Lucian. There's a secret way into the back of the cave from the top of the hill.'

4 _____ 'Don't worry – they won't catch me! And where shall we meet afterwards?'

5 _____ 'Yes, but not both of us. I'll go in by myself.'

6 _____ 'Yes, that's true. So what do you want me to do?'

7 _____ 'And while they're out of the cave, looking for you, I'll get Alexis out through the back. But make sure they don't catch you!'

8 _____ 'And you too, Corinna!'

9 _____ 'I want you to go down by the river, and crash around among the trees, making a lot of noise.'

10 _____ 'Is there? And you think we can get into the cave and get Alexis out that way?'

11 _____ 'At the theatre. Alexis and I will go straight there. Right, let's go. Good luck, Lucian!'

12 _____ 'But Corinna, won't it be better if we both go in?'

2 Use the words below to complete this text about the theatre in Athens.

actors, audience, comedies, dancing, music, play, speeches, stage, terraces, theatre, tragedies

Alexis' _____ was part of the _____ festival in Athens. The _____ stood on the _____ to make their _____, and the _____ sat opposite them on the _____. Some of the plays were _____, or sad plays; others were _____, which had jokes and were about politics. People who went to see the plays could also enjoy watching the _____ and listening to the _____.

3 Here is Magnes telling his Spartan friends what happened in Athens. Complete his report with these linking words.

and / and / because / but / but / how / so / that / until / what / when / who / who

Last night we found a boy _____ was spying on us. We tied him up _____ planned to leave him in the cave _____ the festival was over. Sometime in the night the boy escaped, _____ I don't know _____ he did it. We couldn't warn Hippias _____ he was already back in Athens and in the theatre. A friend told us _____ happened. In one of the actors' speeches, there was a warning _____ a revolution was coming. _____ the actor spoke of danger from men _____ carried long knives under their cloaks, our friends got very worried. They left the theatre, _____ there were soldiers at every exit _____ they were all arrested. Without friends inside Athens, we can do nothing, _____ the revolution has failed, my friends.

65

4 Perhaps this is what some of the characters in the story were thinking. Which six characters were they, and what was happening in the story at that moment?

1 'Ah, here she is now, with her flute. She looks so like her mother! I can see Demetria watching her from the other room, but she doesn't know yet that she's watching her daughter – her very own daughter . . .'

2 'This is a very clever boy. I can't catch him with any of my questions. And his play is good – amusing, but full of interesting ideas too. I can see that his uncle isn't looking forward to the Festival, but I am!'

3 'Shall I ask her to play the flute at this party? She plays so beautifully, and this rich young man will pay her well. We need the money. But it's no good. I can see her angry face. She won't go, I know she won't . . .'

4 'Why didn't he practise more? He nearly dropped the torch when he passed it to me, and it's because of him we lost the race. I hope he's feeling ashamed of himself. I'm going home the other way. I don't want to see him . . .'

5 'This is wonderful! Everyone's laughing at the jokes, and the cow was great – really funny. I *do* hope his play wins. And nobody's looking at me – I'm just a farm boy, in a dirty old coat. The clothes smell terrible, but never mind!'

6 'What's this actor talking about? Watch for danger in party masks . . . long-nosed men . . . long knives . . .? Somebody knows too much! I'm getting out of here at once . . .'

5 How was a boy's life different from a girl's life in ancient Athens? Use these notes to write a short paragraph.

- going out in public
- playing sport
- going to the theatre
- having visitors to the house
- writing plays
- talking about politics

6 The stick-message on page 38 was in groups of 8 letters. Can you find the hidden sentences in these two stick-messages? (The groups are not less than 3, and not more than 8.)

IOBOIOKTUWKTNHTTNHOIIHOIWNKAWNNGNTNG

IYTNTASESHMEAAEANTNM

GTHDTATEMHDONAIFBIKNLIAEK

Now answer these questions about the stick-messages.

1 The same person said both sentences. Who was it?

2 Who was the person speaking to, and when?

3 How was the second sentence useful for Alexis?

7 Here are some new titles for the story. Which one do you like best, and why?

The Night of Long Knives	Carnival Danger
Alexis and the Gadfly	Alexis and Corinna
The Message in the Cave	Enemies of Athens

ABOUT THE AUTHOR

Geoffrey Trease was born in Nottingham, England, in 1909. He always wanted to be a writer. As a boy at school he wrote stories, poems, and a play, and at the age of thirteen, when his father offered him a bicycle, Geoffrey asked for a typewriter instead. He went to Oxford University, but was bored by the teaching, so he left and went to London to work with poor children. After that, he was a journalist, and then a teacher, but when his first novel was published, he became a full-time writer. During his life he wrote more than one hundred books: books for children and for adults, plays, short stories, translations, poems, and biographies. He died in 1998.

His best-known books are his many historical adventure stories for young people. The first of these, *Bows Against the Barons*, published in 1934, tells the story of Robin Hood, the famous outlaw of Sherwood Forest, near Nottingham. Another very popular book is *Cue for Treason*, which is set in England in the time of Shakespeare. Trease's stories are set in many countries, at many different times in history – from ancient Greece, as in *The Crown of Violet*, to the Russian Revolution in *The White Knights of St Petersburg*.

Trease always wanted to give a true picture of life in the past, but it was also important to him that his books had a good story to tell. 'I have a child's enjoyment of a secret passage or galloping horses at midnight,' he said once. 'You've got to believe it all yourself . . .' And this feeling of excitement, wanting to know what happens next, is found in all Geoffrey Trease's stories.

OXFORD BOOKWORMS LIBRARY

Classics • Crime & Mystery • Factfiles • Fantasy & Horror
Human Interest • Playscripts • Thriller & Adventure
True Stories • World Stories

The OXFORD BOOKWORMS LIBRARY provides enjoyable reading in English, with a wide range of classic and modern fiction, non-fiction, and plays. It includes original and adapted texts in seven carefully graded language stages, which take learners from beginner to advanced level. An overview is given on the next pages.

All Stage 1 titles are available as audio recordings, as well as over eighty other titles from Starter to Stage 6. All Starters and many titles at Stages 1 to 4 are specially recommended for younger learners. Every Bookworm is illustrated, and Starters and Factfiles have full-colour illustrations.

The OXFORD BOOKWORMS LIBRARY also offers extensive support. Each book contains an introduction to the story, notes about the author, a glossary, and activities. Additional resources include tests and worksheets, and answers for these and for the activities in the books. There is advice on running a class library, using audio recordings, and the many ways of using Oxford Bookworms in reading programmes. Resource materials are available on the website <www.oup.com/elt/bookworms>.

The *Oxford Bookworms Collection* is a series for advanced learners. It consists of volumes of short stories by well-known authors, both classic and modern. Texts are not abridged or adapted in any way, but carefully selected to be accessible to the advanced student.

You can find details and a full list of titles in the *Oxford Bookworms Library Catalogue* and *Oxford English Language Teaching Catalogues*, and on the website <www.oup.com/elt/bookworms>.

THE OXFORD BOOKWORMS LIBRARY
GRADING AND SAMPLE EXTRACTS

STARTER • 250 HEADWORDS

present simple – present continuous – imperative –
can/cannot, must – *going to* (future) – simple gerunds …

Her phone is ringing – but where is it?

Sally gets out of bed and looks in her bag. No phone. She looks under the bed. No phone. Then she looks behind the door. There is her phone. Sally picks up her phone and answers it. *Sally's Phone*

STAGE 1 • 400 HEADWORDS

… past simple – coordination with *and, but, or* –
subordination with *before, after, when, because, so* …

I knew him in Persia. He was a famous builder and I worked with him there. For a time I was his friend, but not for long. When he came to Paris, I came after him – I wanted to watch him. He was a very clever, very dangerous man. *The Phantom of the Opera*

STAGE 2 • 700 HEADWORDS

… present perfect – *will* (future) – *(don't) have to, must not, could* – comparison of adjectives – simple *if* clauses – past continuous – tag questions – *ask/tell* + infinitive …

While I was writing these words in my diary, I decided what to do. I must try to escape. I shall try to get down the wall outside. The window is high above the ground, but I have to try. I shall take some of the gold with me – if I escape, perhaps it will be helpful later. *Dracula*

STAGE 3 • 1000 HEADWORDS

… should, may – present perfect continuous – *used to* – past perfect –
causative – relative clauses – indirect statements …

Of course, it was most important that no one should see
Colin, Mary, or Dickon entering the secret garden. So Colin
gave orders to the gardeners that they must all keep away
from that part of the garden in future. *The Secret Garden*

STAGE 4 • 1400 HEADWORDS

… past perfect continuous – passive (simple forms) –
would conditional clauses – indirect questions –
relatives with *where/when* – gerunds after prepositions/phrases …

I was glad. Now Hyde could not show his face to the world
again. If he did, every honest man in London would be proud
to report him to the police. *Dr Jekyll and Mr Hyde*

STAGE 5 • 1800 HEADWORDS

… future continuous – future perfect –
passive (modals, continuous forms) –
would have conditional clauses – modals + perfect infinitive …

If he had spoken Estella's name, I would have hit him. I was so
angry with him, and so depressed about my future, that I could
not eat the breakfast. Instead I went straight to the old house.
Great Expectations

STAGE 6 • 2500 HEADWORDS

… passive (infinitives, gerunds) – advanced modal meanings –
clauses of concession, condition

When I stepped up to the piano, I was confident. It was as if I
knew that the prodigy side of me really did exist. And when I
started to play, I was so caught up in how lovely I looked that
I didn't worry how I would sound. *The Joy Luck Club*

Kidnapped

ROBERT LOUIS STEVENSON

Retold by Clare West

'I ran to the side of the ship. "Help, help! Murder!" I screamed, and my uncle slowly turned to look at me. I did not see any more. Already strong hands were pulling me away. Then something hit my head; I saw a great flash of fire, and fell to the ground . . .'

And so begin David Balfour's adventures. He is kidnapped, taken to sea, and meets many dangers. He also meets a friend, Alan Breck. But Alan is in danger himself, on the run from the English army across the wild Highlands of Scotland . . .

Moondial

HELEN CRESSWELL

Retold by John Escott

'Moondial!' As Minty spoke the word, a cold wind went past her, and her ears were filled with a thousand frightened voices. She shut her eyes and put her hands over her ears – and the voices and the wind went away. Minty opened her eyes . . . *and knew that she was in a different morning, not the one she had woken up to.*

And so Minty's strange adventure begins – a journey through time into the past, where she finds Tom, and Sarah . . . and the evil Miss Vole.